HELP WITH HOMEWORK

C000050771

MATHS

Here's a short note for parents:

We recommend that you work through this book with your child, offering guidance and encouragement along the way.

Find a quiet place to sit, preferably at a table, and encourage your child to hold their pencil correctly.

Try to work at your child's pace and avoid spending too long on any one page or activity.

Most of all, emphasize the fun element of what you are doing and enjoy yourselves. You can add a reward sticker to the bottom of each page as you complete it.

Reward sticker!

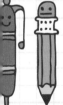

Autumn
Publishing

Count to 100

What numbers are missing from this grid?
Fill in the missing numbers below.

1	2		4	5	6		8	9	10
11		13	14		16	17		19	
21	22	23		25		27	28		30
	32		34		36	37	38	39	40
41		43	44	45			48	49	
51	52		54		56	57	58		60
61	62	63		65	66	67		69	70
71	72	73	74		76		78	79	
81		83		85		87	88	89	90
	92		94	95	96	97		99	

Reward sticker!

Count in 2s

Help the frog get to her lily pad by writing in the missing numbers in the sequence.

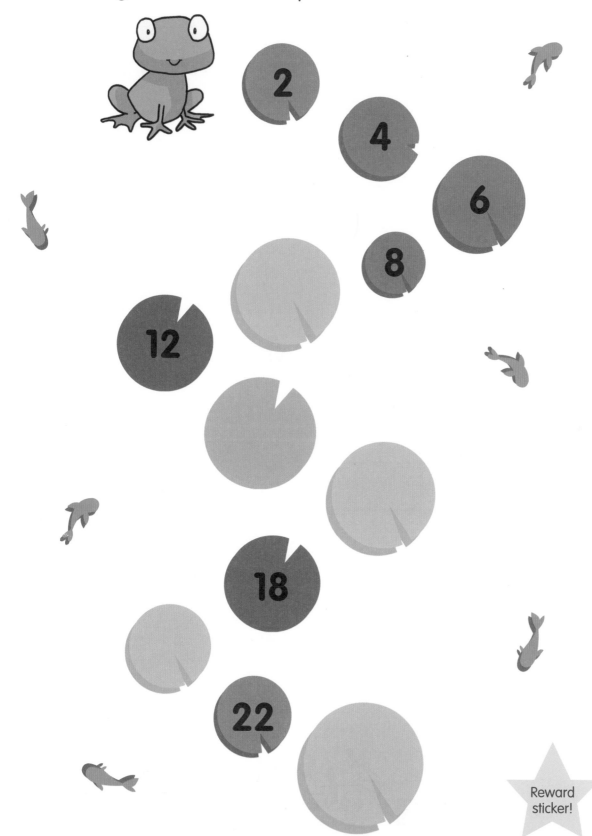

Reward sticker!

One more, one less

Practise adding and subtracting by 1 in the sums below.
Write the answers in the boxes.

7 + 1 = | 8 | 2 - 1 = | 1 |

4 + 1 = | | 8 - 1 = | |

8 + 1 = | | 5 - 1 = | |

3 + 1 = | | 3 - 1 = | |

6 + 1 = | | 7 - 1 = | |

Reward sticker!

4

Grouping

Draw circles to put the bees into groups of 3.

How many groups are there?

How many bees are there altogether?

Draw circles to put these sweets into groups of 4.

How many groups are there?

How many sweets are there altogether?

Reward sticker!

Adding up

Do the additions below, writing the answers in the boxes.

$1 + 2 = $ ⬜ $4 + 8 = $ ⬜

$6 + 5 = $ ⬜ $2 + 10 = $ ⬜

$8 + 1 = $ ⬜ $3 + 5 = $ ⬜

$3 + 3 = $ ⬜ $9 + 3 = $ ⬜

$6 + 8 = $ ⬜ $8 + 8 = $ ⬜

$10 + 10 = $ ⬜ $9 + 9 = $ ⬜

Reward sticker!

Making 10

Put a tick after each question that makes 10. Put a **X** after the ones that don't.

5 + 5   7 + 4

2 + 9  1 + 9

8 + 2   2 + 8

3 + 7   7 + 3

6 + 7   6 + 4

9 + 1   3 + 8

4 + 6   7 + 7

Taking away

Do the subtractions below, writing the answers in the boxes.

5 – 2 = ☐

7 – 2 = ☐

6 – 2 = ☐

13 – 12 = ☐

12 – 6 = ☐

20 – 11 = ☐

7 – 6 = ☐

18 – 9 = ☐

3 – 2 = ☐

16 – 14 = ☐

8 – 5 = ☐

4 – 2 = ☐

Reward sticker!

Making 20

Colour the diamond after every question that makes 20.

12 + 8   12 + 8

13 + 7   19 + 1

20 - 2   10 + 10

24 - 4   11 + 8

15 + 6   14 + 8

16 + 4   26 + 6

25 - 5   15 + 5

Reward sticker!

9

Count in 5s and 10s

Fill in the numbers to help each frog follow its path to the other side of the lily pond.

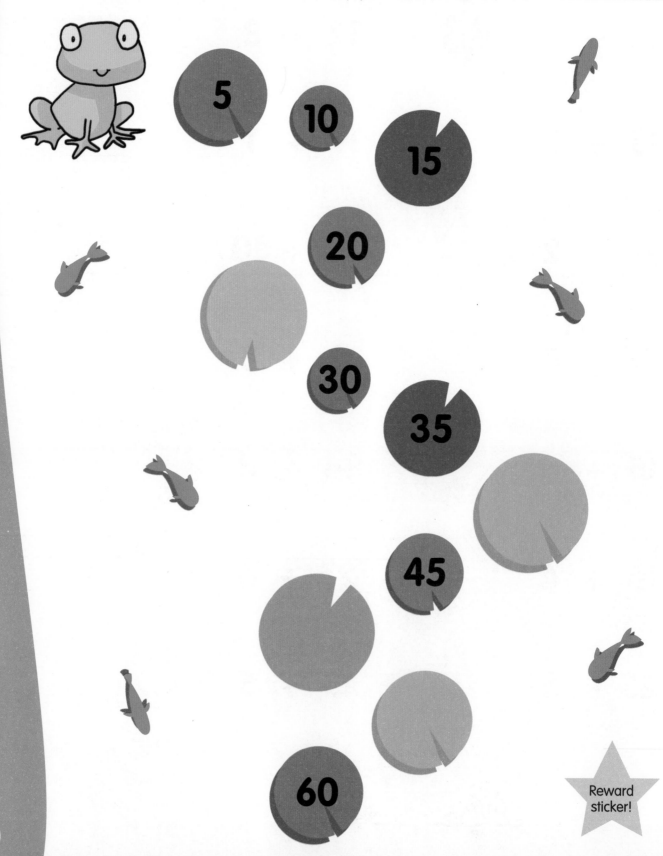

5

10

15

20

30

35

45

60

Reward sticker!

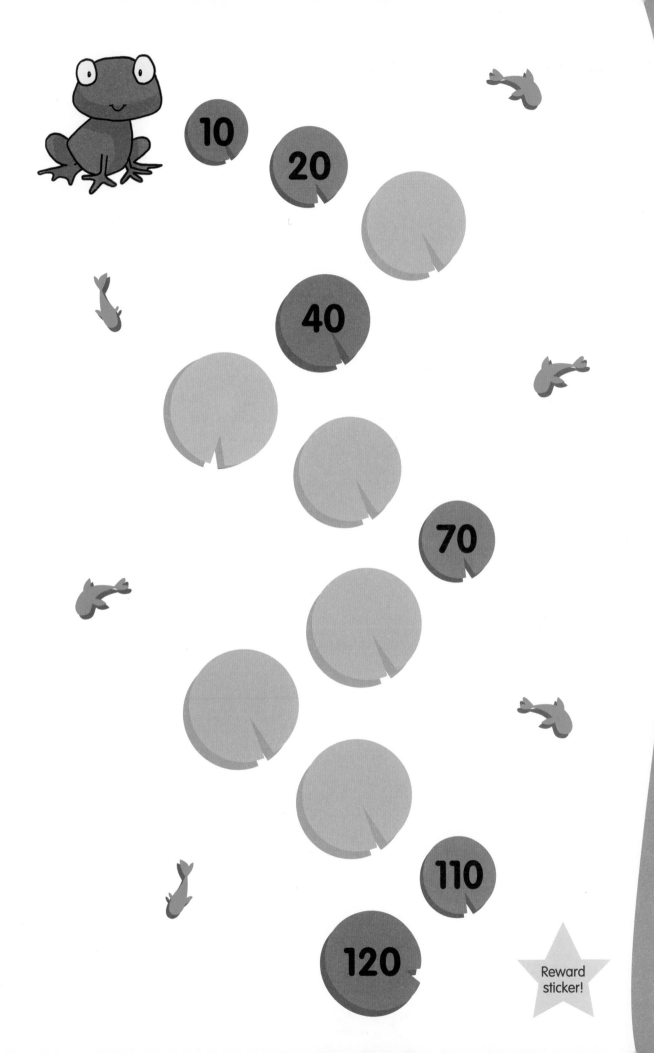

Missing numbers

Fill in the missing numbers below to solve these out-of-this-world addition and subtraction sums.

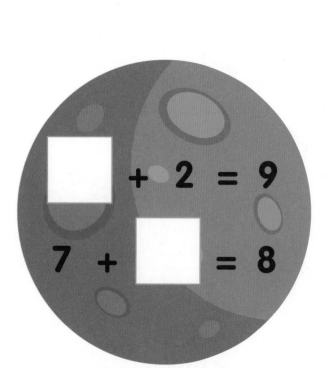

$\square + 2 = 9$

$7 + \square = 8$

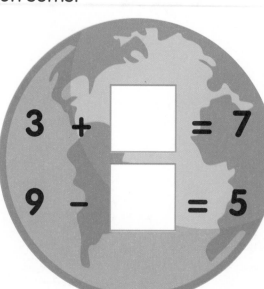

$3 + \square = 7$

$9 - \square = 5$

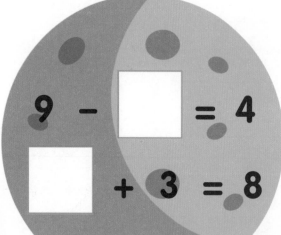

$9 - \square = 4$

$\square + 3 = 8$

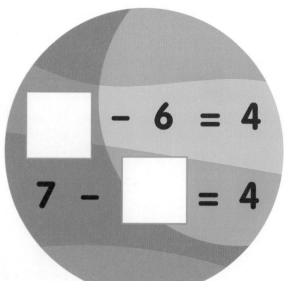

$\square - 6 = 4$

$7 - \square = 4$

Reward sticker!

$\Box + 12 = 19$

$7 + \Box = 15$

$3 + \Box = 20$

$8 + \Box = 17$

$\Box - 6 = 11$

$16 - \Box = 11$

$19 - \Box = 14$

$\Box + 3 = 18$

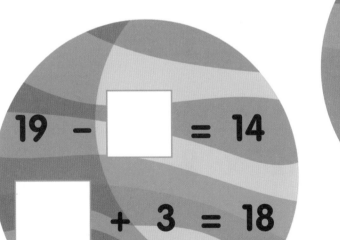

Reward sticker!

Multiplying by 2

Complete the 2 times multiplication sums below.
Write the answers in the boxes.

1 x 2 = ☐   7 x 2 = ☐

2 x 2 = ☐   8 x 2 = ☐

3 x 2 = ☐   9 x 2 = ☐

4 x 2 = ☐   10 x 2 = ☐

5 x 2 = ☐   11 x 2 = ☐

6 x 2 = ☐   12 x 2 = ☐

Reward sticker!

Number patterns x2

Colour each square that shows an answer from the last page. This is the pattern of your 2 times table! Can you carry on the pattern all the way to 100?

1	2	3	4	5	6	7	8	9	10
11	12	13	14	15	16	17	18	19	20
21	22	23	24	25	26	27	28	29	30
31	32	33	34	35	36	37	38	39	40
41	42	43	44	45	46	47	48	49	50
51	52	53	54	55	56	57	58	59	60
61	62	63	64	65	66	67	68	69	70
71	72	73	74	75	76	77	78	79	80
81	82	83	84	85	86	87	88	89	90
91	92	93	94	95	96	97	98	99	100

Reward sticker!

Multiplying by 5

Complete the 5 times multiplication sums below.
Write the answers in the boxes.

1 x 5 = ☐   7 x 5 = ☐

2 x 5 = ☐   8 x 5 = ☐

3 x 5 = ☐   9 x 5 = ☐

4 x 5 = ☐   10 x 5 = ☐

5 x 5 = ☐   11 x 5 = ☐

6 x 5 = ☐   12 x 5 = ☐

Reward sticker!

Number patterns x5

Colour each square that shows an answer from the last page.
This is the pattern of your 5 times table! Can you carry on
the pattern all the way to 100?

1	2	3	4	5	6	7	8	9	10
11	12	13	14	15	16	17	18	19	20
21	22	23	24	25	26	27	28	29	30
31	32	33	34	35	36	37	38	39	40
41	42	43	44	45	46	47	48	49	50
51	52	53	54	55	56	57	58	59	60
61	62	63	64	65	66	67	68	69	70
71	72	73	74	75	76	77	78	79	80
81	82	83	84	85	86	87	88	89	90
91	92	93	94	95	96	97	98	99	100

Reward sticker!

Multiplying by 10

Complete the 10 times multiplication sums below.
Write the answers in the boxes.

1 x 10 =

7 x 10 =

2 x 10 =

8 x 10 =

3 x 10 =

9 x 10 =

4 x 10 =

10 x 10 =

5 x 10 =

11 x 10 =

6 x 10 =

12 x 10 =

Reward sticker!

18

Number patterns x10

Colour each square that shows an answer from the last page. This is the pattern of your 10 times table! How is the pattern different to the 2 times and 5 times tables?

1	2	3	4	5	6	7	8	9	10
11	12	13	14	15	16	17	18	19	20
21	22	23	24	25	26	27	28	29	30
31	32	33	34	35	36	37	38	39	40
41	42	43	44	45	46	47	48	49	50
51	52	53	54	55	56	57	58	59	60
61	62	63	64	65	66	67	68	69	70
71	72	73	74	75	76	77	78	79	80
81	82	83	84	85	86	87	88	89	90
91	92	93	94	95	96	97	98	99	100

Reward sticker!

Double bubble

Double the numbers in each of the bubbles below.
Hint: double 4 is the same as 4 + 4.

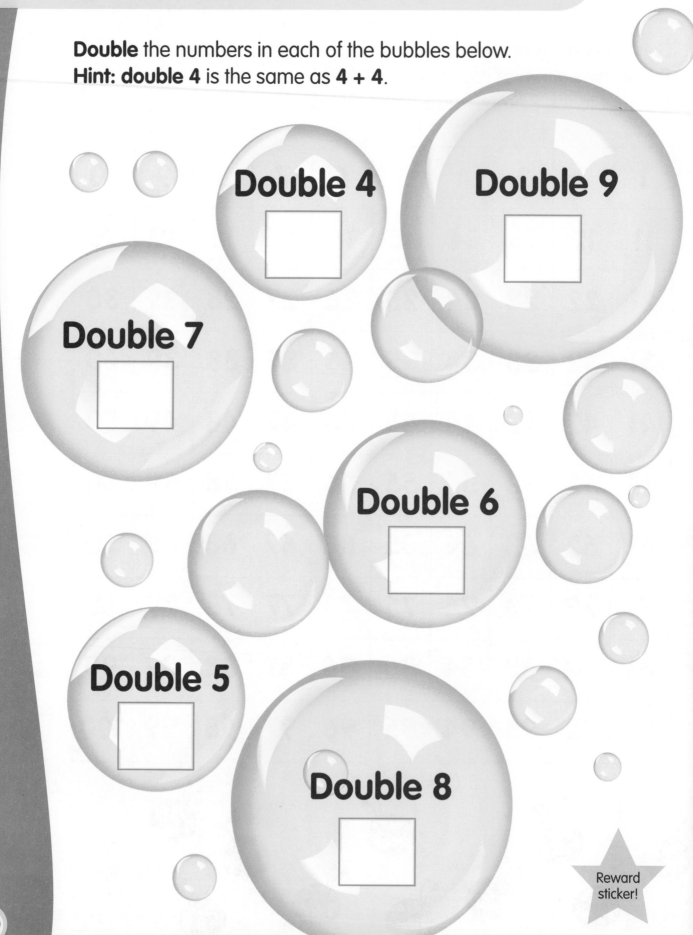

Double 4

Double 9

Double 7

Double 6

Double 5

Double 8

Reward sticker!

2D shapes

A 2D (two-dimensional) shape is a shape that has length and width, but no depth. This means that it is flat.

Count all of the **squares** below. How many are there altogether? Write your answer in the box.

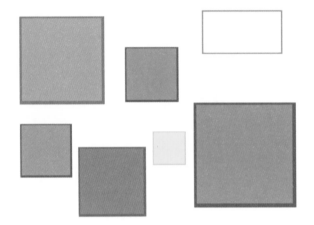

Count all of the **rectangles** below. How many are there altogether? Write your answer in the box.

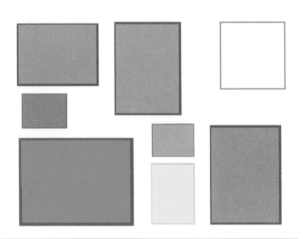

Count all of the **circles** below. How many are there altogether? Write your answer in the box.

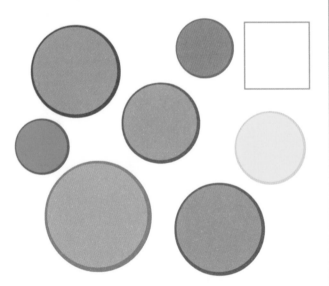

Count all of the **triangles** below. How many are there altogether? Write your answer in the box.

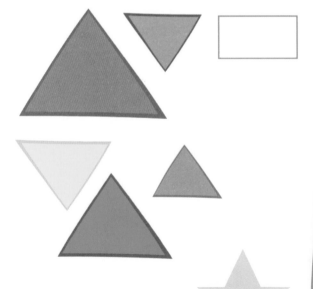

Reward sticker!

21

Halves

Shade in **half** of each of the shapes below.
The first shape has been done for you.

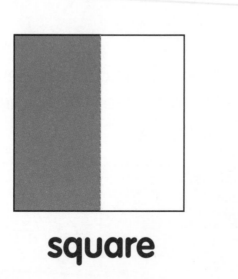

square

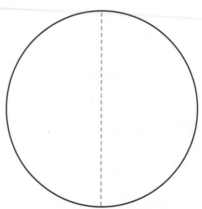

circle

rectangle

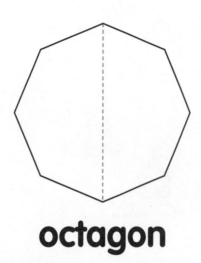

octagon

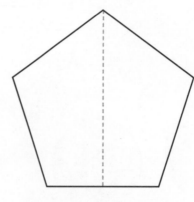

pentagon

Reward sticker!

Draw a ring around **half** of the objects for each of the below.
Then read the questions and write your answers in the boxes.

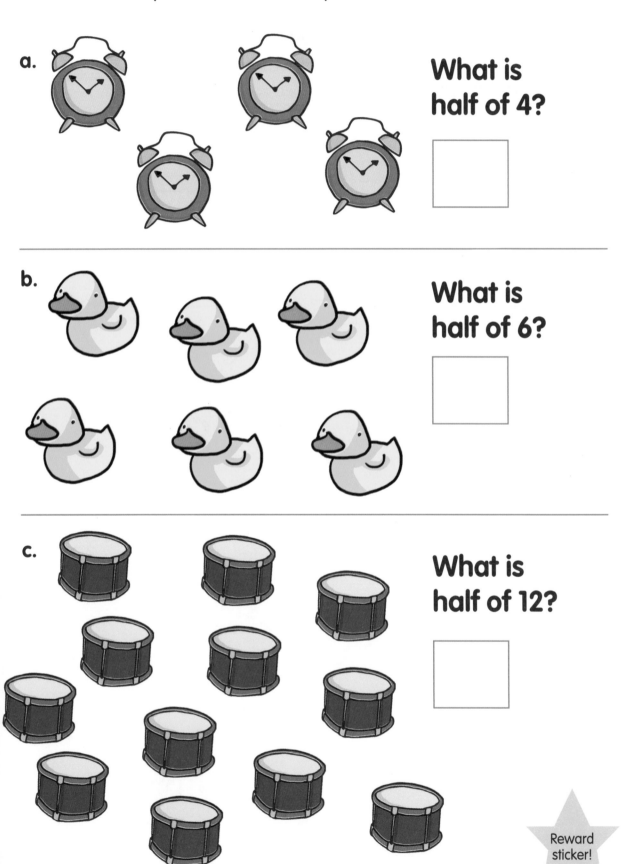

a. **What is half of 4?**

b. **What is half of 6?**

c. **What is half of 12?**

Reward
sticker!

Quarters

Shade in a **quarter** of each of the shapes below.
The first shape has been done for you.

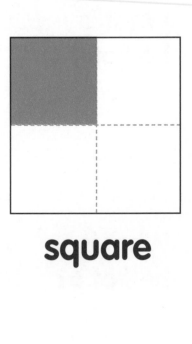

square

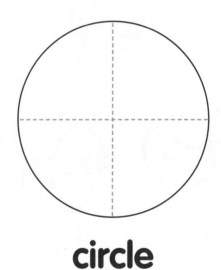

circle

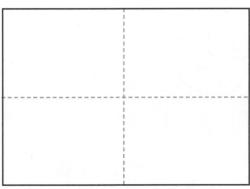

rectangle

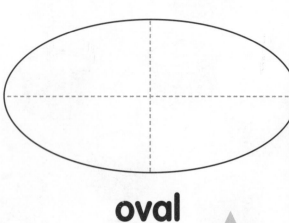

oval

Draw a ring around a **quarter** of the objects for each of the below.
Then read the questions and write your answers in the boxes.

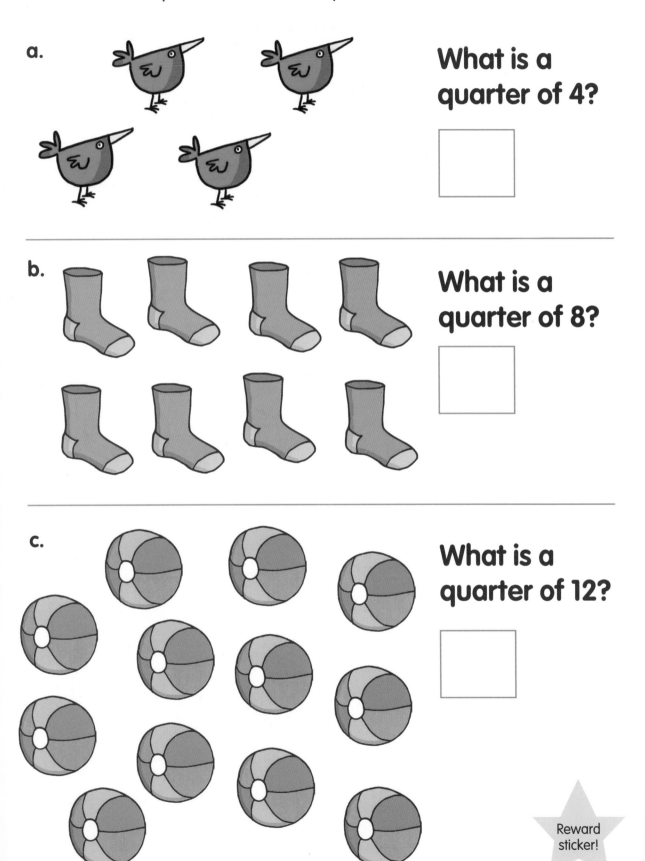

a.

**What is a
quarter of 4?**

b.

**What is a
quarter of 8?**

c.

**What is a
quarter of 12?**

Coins

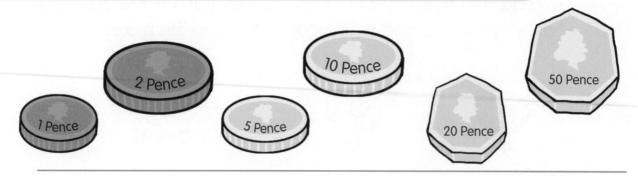

---

a. What two coins are these?

____ and ____

How much are they worth in total?

---

b. What two coins are these?

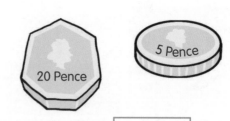

____ and ____

How much are they worth in total?

---

c. What two coins are these?

____ and ____

How much are they worth in total?

Reward sticker!

3D shapes

A 3D (three-dimensional) shape is a shape that has length, width and depth. Take a look at the 3D shapes below.

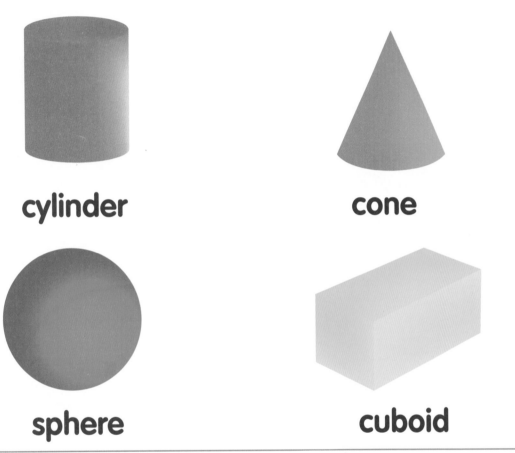

cylinder

cone

sphere

cuboid

This is a face

There are 6 faces on a cube.

How many faces does a cuboid have?

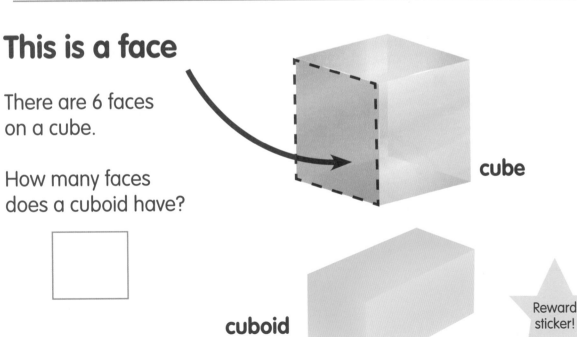

cube

cuboid

Reward sticker!

Colour by shapes

Follow the code to colour this picture.
Choose your own colours where there are no code symbols.

triangle	circle	square	star
light blue	light green	dark blue	dark green

Reward sticker!

Number patterns

Look carefully at these number cards.

1 2 3 4 5 6 7 8 9 10

Then, use the cards to complete the number patterns below.

a.
 2
 4
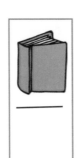 ___
 ___
 10

b.
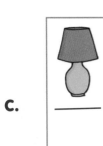 ___
 3
 ___
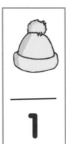 7
 ___

c.
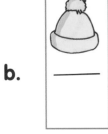 ___
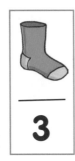 ___
 3
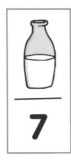 ___
 1

d.
 ___
 ___
 8
 7
 ___

Reward sticker!

Mental maths

Answer the sums below in your head.
Write the answers in the boxes.

4 + 5 + 6 =

19 − 8 + 2 =

5 + 10 − 7 =

20 − 6 + 3 =

17 − 3 − 3 =

18 − 12 + 4 =

Reward sticker!

Answers:

Page 2: Count to 100

1	2	**3**	4	5	6	**7**	8	9	10
11	**12**	13	14	**15**	16	17	**18**	19	**20**
21	22	23	**24**	25	**26**	27	28	**29**	30
31	32	**33**	34	**35**	36	37	38	39	40
41	**42**	43	44	45	**46**	**47**	48	49	**50**
51	52	**53**	54	**55**	56	57	58	**59**	60
61	62	63	**64**	65	66	67	**68**	69	70
71	72	73	74	**75**	76	**77**	78	79	**80**
81	**82**	83	**84**	85	**86**	87	88	89	90
91	92	**93**	94	95	96	97	**98**	99	**100**

Page 3: Count up in 2s

2, 4, 6, 8, **10**, 12, **14**, **16**, 18, **20**, 22, **24**

Page 4: One more, one less

4 + 1 = **5**   8 – 1 = **7**
8 + 1 = **9**   5 – 1 = **4**
3 + 1 = **4**   3 – 1 = **2**
6 + 1 = **7**   7 – 1 = **6**

Page 5: Grouping

5 groups of bees, 15 bees altogether
3 groups of sweets, 12 sweets altogether

Page 6: Adding up

1 + 2 = **3**   4 + 8 = **12**
6 + 5 = **11**   2 + 10 = **12**
8 + 1 = **9**   3 + 5 = **8**
3 + 3 = **6**   9 + 3 = **12**
6 + 8 = **14**   8 + 8 = **16**
10 + 10 = **20**   9 + 9 = **18**

Page 7: Making 10

5 + 5 ✓   7 + 4 ✗
2 + 9 ✗   1 + 9 ✓
8 + 2 ✓   2 + 8 ✓
3 + 7 ✓   7 + 3 ✓
6 + 7 ✗   6 + 4 ✓
9 + 1 ✓   3 + 8 ✗
4 + 6 ✓   7 + 7 ✗

Page 8: Taking away

5 – 2 = **3**   7 – 2 = **5**
6 – 2 = **4**   13 – 12 = **1**
12 – 6 = **6**   20 – 11 = **9**
7 – 6 = **1**   18 – 9 = **9**
3 – 2 = **1**   16 – 14 = **2**
8 – 5 = **3**   4 – 2 = **2**

Page 9: Making 20

12 + 8 ◆   12 + 8 ◆
13 + 7 ◆   19 + 1 ◆
20 – 2 ◇   10 + 10 ◆
24 – 4 ◆   11 + 8 ◇
15 + 6 ◇   14 + 8 ◇
16 + 4 ◆   26 + 6 ◇
25 – 5 ◆   15 + 5 ◆

Pages 10-11: Count in 5s and 10s

5, 10, 15, 20, **25**, 30, 35, **40**, 45, **50**, **55**, 60
10, 20, **30**, 40, **50**, **60**, 70, **80**, **90**, **100**, 110, 120

Pages 12-13: Missing numbers

7 + 2 = 9   7 + **1** = 8
3 + **4** = 7   9 – **4** = 5
9 – **5** = 4   **5** + 3 = 8
10 – 6 = 4   7 – **3** = 4
7 + 12 = 19   7 + **8** = 15
3 + **17** = 20   8 + **9** = 17
17 – 6 = 11   16 – **5** = 11
19 – **5** = 14   **15** + 3 = 18

Page 14: Multiplying by 2

1 x 2 = **2**   7 x 2 = **14**
2 x 2 = **4**   8 x 2 = **16**
3 x 2 = **6**   9 x 2 = **18**
4 x 2 = **8**   10 x 2 = **20**
5 x 2 = **10**   11 x 2 = **22**
6 x 2 = **12**   12 x 2 = **24**

Answers:

Page 15: Number patterns x2

1	2	3	4	5	6	7	8	9	10
11	12	13	14	15	16	17	18	19	20
21	22	23	24	25	26	27	28	29	30
31	32	33	34	35	36	37	38	39	40
41	42	43	44	45	46	47	48	49	50
51	52	53	54	55	56	57	58	59	60
61	62	63	64	65	66	67	68	69	70
71	72	73	74	75	76	77	78	79	80
81	82	83	84	85	86	87	88	89	90
91	92	93	94	95	96	97	98	99	100

Page 16: Multiplying by 5

$1 \times 5 = 5$ $7 \times 5 = 35$
$2 \times 5 = 10$ $8 \times 5 = 40$
$3 \times 5 = 15$ $9 \times 5 = 45$
$4 \times 5 = 20$ $10 \times 5 = 50$
$5 \times 5 = 25$ $11 \times 5 = 55$
$6 \times 5 = 30$ $12 \times 5 = 60$

Page 17: Number patterns x5

1	2	3	4	5	6	7	8	9	10
11	12	13	14	15	16	17	18	19	20
21	22	23	24	25	26	27	28	29	30
31	32	33	34	35	36	37	38	39	40
41	42	43	44	45	46	47	48	49	50
51	52	53	54	55	56	57	58	59	60
61	62	63	64	65	66	67	68	69	70
71	72	73	74	75	76	77	78	79	80
81	82	83	84	85	86	87	88	89	90
91	92	93	94	95	96	97	98	99	100

Page 18: Multiplying by 10

$1 \times 10 = 10$ $7 \times 10 = 70$
$2 \times 10 = 20$ $8 \times 10 = 80$
$3 \times 10 = 30$ $9 \times 10 = 90$
$4 \times 10 = 40$ $10 \times 10 = 100$
$5 \times 10 = 50$ $11 \times 10 = 110$
$6 \times 10 = 60$ $12 \times 10 = 120$

Page 19: Number patterns x10

1	2	3	4	5	6	7	8	9	10
11	12	13	14	15	16	17	18	19	20
21	22	23	24	25	26	27	28	29	30
31	32	33	34	35	36	37	38	39	40
41	42	43	44	45	46	47	48	49	50
51	52	53	54	55	56	57	58	59	60
61	62	63	64	65	66	67	68	69	70
71	72	73	74	75	76	77	78	79	80
81	82	83	84	85	86	87	88	89	90
91	92	93	94	95	96	97	98	99	100

Page 20: Double bubble

Double 4 = 8
Double 9 = 18
Double 7 = 14
Double 6 = 12
Double 5 = 10
Double 8 = 16

Page 21: 2D Shapes

6 squares 7 rectangles
7 circles 5 triangles

Pages 22-23: Halves

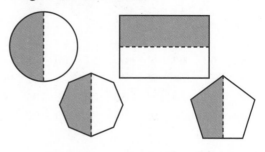

a. 2 b. 3 c. 6

Pages 24-25: Quarters

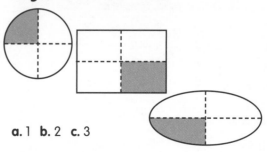

a. 1 b. 2 c. 3

Page 26: Coins

a. 1p + 10p = 11p
b. 20p + 5p = 25p
c. 2p + 50p = 52p

Page 27: 3D shapes

The cuboid has 6 faces.

Page 29: Number patterns

a. 2, 4, 6, 8, 10
b. 1, 3, 5, 7, 9
c. 5, 4, 3, 2, 1
d. 10, 9, 8, 7, 6

Page 30: Mental maths

$4 + 5 + 6 = 15$
$19 - 8 + 2 = 13$
$5 + 10 - 7 = 8$

$20 - 6 + 3 = 17$
$17 - 3 - 3 = 11$
$18 - 12 + 4 = 10$